Usborne
Wipe-Clean
Money

Use your wipe-clean pen to trace and write to help the monsters learn about money.

This Mushy Monster Cake costs 4 pugs.

Yay! I've got the right money.

Oh no! I can't afford it.

Spud

Spike

Munchy

Illustrated by Gareth Williams.

Designed by Keith Newell. Words by Jane Bingham.

Counting coins

The monsters are counting their pugs before they go shopping.
Can you help them? Spud has already counted his.

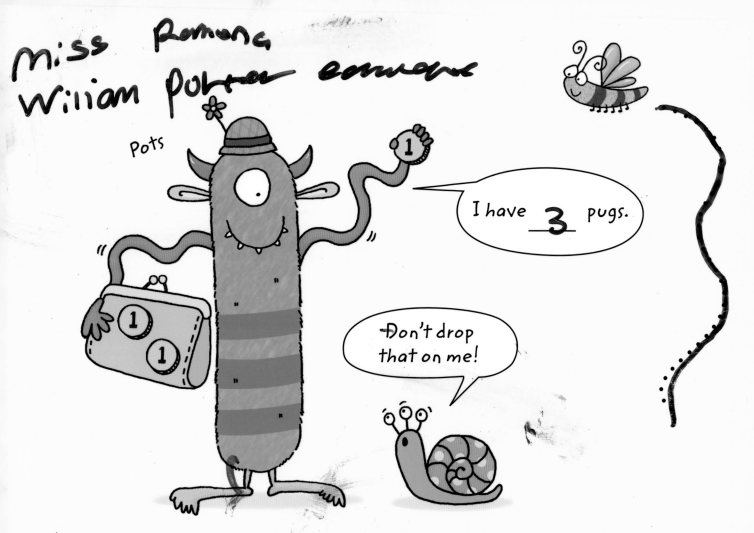

Pots

I have **3** pugs.

Don't drop that on me!

Pup wants Flutter to look after his money for him. Draw a line through Pup's coins and draw the extra coins in Flutter's purse.

Now Pup has given me his money, I have ____ pugs.

Pup

Flutter

Which monster on these pages has the most money? Draw a star next to him or her.

Stacks of snacks

The first thing the monsters want to do is buy some snacks.
Draw a line between each monster and the snack he or she can buy.
(They need to pay the exact money shown on the machines.)

Spike's things cost 4 pugs, plus 2 pugs, plus 2 pugs. Fill in the answer to his sum.

MONSTER SALE!

4 pugs

2 pugs

2 pugs

Weeee!

$$4 + 2 + 2 = \boxed{}$$

The items in Munchy's cart cost 3 pugs, plus 3 pugs, plus 2 pugs.

Can you draw three things in Munchy's cart?

Hey! Wait for me!

3 pugs

2 pugs

3 pugs

Now fill in the answer to his sum.

$$3 + 3 + 2 = \boxed{}$$

Playing pirates

After their shopping trip, the monsters play pirates, using pugs as treasure. Help them share out their pugs so they each have an equal amount.

Draw coins in the treasure chests on this page so each monster has 5 pugs.

Pots has 2 pugs, so he needs
_____ more pugs to equal 5.

2 + ☐ = 5

Slurpy has 3 pugs, so he needs
_____ more pugs to equal 5.

3 + ☐ = ☐

Bumper Cars
2 pugs

$5 - 2 =$ ☐

Teacup Ride
1 pug

Too fast for me!

$5 - 1 =$ ☐

Birthday money

Can you help these monsters count their birthday money?
Some have 1 pug coins, some have 5 pug coins, and some have both.

One 5 pug coin is equal to five 1 pug coins.

I have _____ pugs.

I have _____ pugs.

I have _____.

5 + 2 = ☐   5 + 5 = ☐

Now find the monsters with the same amount of birthday money. Draw a line between each pair.

I've got loads of money!

Draw a star next to the monster who isn't in a pair.

At a café

The monsters are playing waiters and customers at a café.
Each customer has a 5 pug coin to spend and needs some change.
Work out the change each customer needs. The first one has been done for you.

Each customer has one 5 pug coin to spend.

Remember!
One 5 pug coin equals five 1 pug coins.

Scary Pop only costs 2 pugs, so here is your **3** pugs change.

2 pugs

After Curly has taken 2 pugs away from 5, he needs to give 3 pugs back to Spike.

5 – 2 = ☐

How much change do Flutter and Pots need? Draw the right number of coins on each tray. Then fill in the number and complete the sum.

Gloopy Glug only costs 3 pugs. You need ____ pugs change.

3 pugs

5 – 3 = ☐

Hic!

Funky Fizz costs 4 pugs, so you need ____ pug change.

4 pugs

5 – 4 = ☐

More kinds of coins

The monsters are counting the money they've saved in their monster banks. They have three different kinds of coins. Can you spot seven 5 pug coins and three 10 pug coins on this page?

One 10 pug coin is equal to two 5 pug coins or ten 1 pug coins.

Count how many pugs each monster has.

I have _____ pugs.

I have _____ pugs.

I have _____ pugs.

5 + 1 = ☐   5 + 5 = ☐   10 + 1 = ☐

Monster hats

Flutter and her friends want to buy some hats for a party.
Connect the dots to complete the hats. Then draw a line
between each monster and the hat he or she can buy.

Draw a square around the hat that is too expensive for any monster to buy.

Coin exchange machines

The monsters want to exchange their heavy coins for a few that are easier to carry. Count the number of pugs in each bag. Then look at the amount each machine delivers. Can you find the amounts that match?

Monster market

Flutter and her friends are buying fruit at the market.
Can you help them? You can look back through the book for help.

Monster melons
6 pugs each

ugly fruit
8 pugs each

Purple pineapples
7 pugs each

What's the most expensive fruit
Flutter can buy? Draw a line
from the fruit to her basket.

If Goggle and Pup add their money
together, what can they buy? Draw
a line from the fruit to their basket.

5 + 1 + 1 = ☐   2 + 4 = ☐